THE
KRYSTAL
PROMISE

THE KRYSTAL PROMISE

Blaine M. Yorgason & Brenton G. Yorgason

· B O O K C R A F T · S A L T L A K E C I T Y , U T A H ·

Library of Congress Catalog Card Number: 81-69420
ISBN 0-88494-437-9

2nd Printing, 1982

Lithographed in the United States of America
PUBLISHERS PRESS
Salt Lake City, Utah

For Lyla—

who gave more than she can know

MY DAUGHTER

Today a little child,
One I call my
Daughter,
Threw her arms
Around
My leg, and
Squeezed.

I had just opened the door,
Coming home,
And she ran to
Be there
First,
To hold her
Daddy.

But I was tired,
Head hurting,
There were calls to be made,
Then a meeting.
And, oh yes,
She was *covered* with
Strawberry jam.

So I tousled her hair while
Disengaging
Her arms.
My suit must stay
Clean,
And I needed
To hurry!

But her voice,
From behind,
Caught me, tugging—

"Sweetheart,"
I snapped, half turning,
Half disgusted,
"I don't have time. . . ."

Then her eyes, deep and
Blue,
Questioned,
Hurting—
Daddy,
Don't you love me
Anymore?

Came a loneliness then,
Deep inside,
And in the hallway mirror
I felt a
House,
Windows vacant,
Broken . . .

Forever hollow and
Deserted,
Filled with empty echoes
Of silenced love,
Where nothing touched
Because nothing
Cared.

"Oh no!" I cried. "I didn't mean . . ."

And then my jam-covered
Sweetheart,
Running toward my
Anguished cry,
Threw sticky arms around my neck,
Pressed sticky lips tight to
A whiskered wall.

And in the mirror,
Grateful time,
Tears and
Touching,
Love and jam, and
Forgiveness smeared all
Over me.

My dear little girl,
Could ever a man be
More blessed,
Than to be touched and held,
Squeezed and kissed,
By his loving, sticky
Daughter?

How much I love you!

Your Daddy

—Blaine M. Yorgason

ONE

1

Whuuumph! The powerful concussion was like a minor bomb explosion. More startled than frightened, Laura swung back from the stove where she was cooking breakfast just as the interior of the converted bus burst into flame. Instantly, fire was everywhere. The walls, the floor, the ceiling — even the air seemed on fire.

Suddenly Laura found herself in the hallway of the camper, cut off from the rest of her family. The surging, billowing flames cut off her view of the front of the bus, and she had no idea what was happening to her children.

Instinctively, desperately, she ducked her head, covered her face with her forearms, and plunged into the actual inferno. After taking only two steps she was driven back by the intensity of the heat. A feeling of horror seized her as she realized that she could not get to her family, not that way.

"Get out!" she screamed, "Ray, get the children out of the bus!"

But there was no response. No sound but the roaring of the fire.

"Oh, God," she pleaded desperately, "what am I going to do? Help my family to . . ."

Now the flames were closer, actually billowing around her, and Laura instinctively stepped backward. As she did so she bumped into a child, a child who was standing behind her, and a prompting came forcefully into her mind! "Get her out!"

But with the micro-second speed of thought, her mind reverted to her babies—four-year-old Jenni and eighteen-month-old Krystal. What about them? They needed her! Still, Ray had been playing with the two smallest children only seconds before the explosion. Surely he would get Jenni and Krystal out!

Laura's reasoning made perfect sense. Ray was at the front of the bus and he would take care of things there. Yet deep inside she knew, with terrifying certainty, that when the fire was over one of her babies would be dead. This must be what her feelings of foreboding had been about.

Once more she felt the child behind her, and once more the prompting came, even more forcefully: "Get her out! Now!"

This time Laura did not hesitate. She turned, grabbed the little girl (who turned out to be ten-year-old Kari), and began pushing her down the hall toward the emergency exit in the rear of the bus. And as they ran, Laura found her mind working with startling clarity. "I'll take Kari out at the back," she thought, "and then I'll hurry around to the front of the bus and help Ray with the other five children."

The flames were now billowing above their heads, Kari's hair was beginning to singe, and Laura realized that she had to hurry. But as she pushed her daughter across the bed toward the exit door, she was suddenly enveloped by the most horrifying feeling she had ever experienced.

"Krystal!" she screamed. "Oh, Krystal!"

Quickly she spun around and again looked back, attempting to stare through the raging flames, doing her utmost to see down the hall. Was Krystal still there, on the bed? Were her little pink flannel pajamas . . . ?

"Oh, dear Father in Heaven," she silently cried, "I can't stand the thought of my little babies being in all that fire! Please . . . oh, please . . ."

And then there was a tearing within her, a terrible wrenching, and as Laura mouthed Krystal's name she felt what seemed like an actual part of her, something deep inside, being torn out, leaving her. Somehow she knew that one of her babies' spirits — no, *Krystal's spirit* — had left her body. Somehow she knew that her beloved little baby Krystal was dead.

Oh, how she longed to run back through the bus, to see if what she had felt was true! But the terrible wall of flame prevented her from trying — she would never make it. It could not be done. But it was true! Krystal was . . .

Again her rational mind took over. "Don't worry. You can't feel things like that. Krystal's fine! Ray got her and Jenni and the other children out of the front. He would never leave the bus without the baby. Now stop worrying!"

Kari's screams brought Laura's attention back to her older daughter. "Mom, the fire's right here! Open the door! Hurry!"

Laura glanced upward, saw the burning flames over their heads, pushed open the door, and she and Kari jumped safely to the ground. Then, with speed she didn't know that she possessed, Laura ran around to the front of the bus, screaming over and over, "Where are my babies?"

Sliding to a halt near the front door, she looked quickly around and saw Jenni. Good! Now where was Krystal? Where . . . oh, please . . . ! *Where* was her baby?

Could she have been right? She wondered frantically. Could it be true that her beloved little daughter was still in the heart of that horrible holocaust?

Deep within, she knew. And yet, oh, how she hoped and prayed that she was wrong!

As Laura felt the scorching heat searing into her face and the terror searing into her heart, her mind flashed back to just forty-eight hours before, to a conversation she had had with her husband. Now, as the flames leaped before her, consuming the bus, it was almost as though she was slipping back through time, shutting out the fire as she lived again those first few moments of fear.

"Ray, please!" she pleaded, "I'm frightened! No, I *don't* know what's wrong. I just have this terrible feeling. I've had it all morning, and . . . well, yes, I know, sweetheart. It's just that . . ."

With her ear to the kitchen phone, Laura listened for a moment while her husband spoke and then did her best to smile. "Yes, Ray, I know we've talked about it before, and I know that nothing has happened. Only . . . what if this time is different? Sweetheart, I can't tell you how empty and lonely I feel, and I don't know why. I hate this feeling! Can you come home for lunch? Please try, okay? And, Ray, thank you for understanding. I love you, too. 'Bye."

Laura hung up the telephone and stared for a moment out of the window, wondering, worrying. Inside of her she ached as though something terrible had occurred. Yet nothing like that had happened; at least, nothing that involved her babies. And that was where her fears centered—on her two youngest daughters, Jenni and Krystal. Especially those fears focused on Krystal.

Laura sat down, leaned forward in her kitchen chair, placed her chin in her hands, and let her eyes devour her two youngest daughters. Oh, how she loved those little girls! Oh, how . . .

For a moment Laura thought guiltily about all of the things she needed to do—the breakfast dishes sitting in the sink, the spot on the floor where Krystal had spilled her milk, the unmade bed in her room. There was also the rest of the fruit to bottle, and the packing for their camping trip. Momentarily Laura had guilt feelings as she sat there. But how could she possibly concentrate on such things when she felt this fear, this nameless dread, about her babies?

Now, as Jenni and Krystal made a game of grabbing at particles of dust dancing in the sunlight before them, laughing as the tiny specks evaded their little fingers, Laura looked at them and felt again the dreadful stirrings within her heart. What could it be? Why on earth should she be feeling . . . ?

The chiming of the doorbell interrupted Laura's thoughts. For a moment she simply stared, afraid that the caller might be bringing news of one of her other children, news that would destroy the completeness and security of her family. But no, she was being silly. It was a beautiful day, the sun was shining, they were all in good health, and she had everything to be thankful for. It was definitely time she took control of her thoughts, she knew that. She had to. So, shrugging her shoulders, she forced a smile back onto her face and pushed herself to her feet. Krystal, always anxious to open the door, was ahead of her, and Laura watched with a kind of embarrassed amusement as the child scampered outside to greet the visitor.

The caller was their mailman, Charles Murray. By the time Laura reached the door he had put down his package, had picked Krystal up, and was spinning around playfully with the little girl in his arms. Krystal was laughing and grabbing at his ears, and Laura could not tell who was enjoying the game more, Krystal or the mailman. Yet enjoying it they were, for Charles was laughing and carrying on every bit as much as Krystal was.

As Laura watched the excitement in her baby's eyes, she realized again just how much fulfillment she had received during the eighteen months Krystal had been in their home. In her years of bearing and rearing children, she had never known a child who was quite like this little girl. Krystal was outgoing, bubbly, thoroughly effervescent, and with her locks of shining golden-white hair and her piercing dark eyes, she was beautiful. In fact, she was . . .

"Laura," Charles said, interrupting her reverie, "this little lady is really something! I'd surely enjoy having a daughter like her. Hey, Krystal, come be my little girl, okay?"

But Krystal, still smiling, shook her head no and then squirmed to get down. Reluctantly the postman leaned over and placed the child on the ground, where she waved, turned, and scampered into the house.

"Honestly, Laura," he said, "I'd give anything if LaRue and I could have a little girl, especially if she could be like Krystal. She is really fun!"

"Just be patient, Charles," Laura replied, "and keep exercising your faith. If there is a girl somewhere who should be yours, Heavenly Father will send her to you."

"Yes, I know he will, Laura. Sometimes, though, it's pretty hard to have patience. I know the good Lord always does what is best, but it would surely be easier if he'd let us know why we always seem to have boys. They about wear LaRue out."

Laura laughed. "And I wish I knew why we've always had girls. It's a good thing we adopted Scott. We'd never have gotten him otherwise. For some reason we just don't seem to have what it takes to order boys. Anyway, without him we'd be in real trouble around here. In fact," and Laura laughed again, "we're usually in trouble out here anyway."

Charles laughed with her but then grew serious. "You know," he said quietly, "you and Ray have really had your share of problems. Your house burned down, and I know you've had a lot of health problems. LaRue told me that you've had . . . ah . . . well, quite a few miscarriages."

"Yes, Charles, we've had several."

"Well, then it's no wonder the Lord gave you someone like Krystal. You've earned her."

"I guess so. She's a very special child. But so are our other children. And so are yours. In fact, as Ray is always reminding me, everyone is special in one way or another."

This time Charles laughed. "You're right, Laura. Though in my opinion some of us are a darn sight more special than others."

They laughed together then, and when their little joke was over, Charles stooped down and picked up the package he was delivering.

"This is for Tami, Laura. Special delivery. Must be important."

"Out here in the desert, Charles, *everything* is important. Especially to a brand new teenager! Thank you for bringing it out."

"No problem, Laura. You have a good day now, all right? And if you decide you have too many daughters, just give us a call. I'll trade any one of my boys straight across for Krystal, and I'll throw in a hundred dollars to boot."

"Wow! There are days when that would tempt me, Charles. But in all fairness, don't hold your breath."

"I won't." He grinned as he hoisted himself up into his jeep.

"I won't. Say, tell Ray hello. Remind him that he owes Jesse Ecker, Dennis Martin, and me a good fishing trip."

As Charles drove off, Laura waved and turned back inside, still concerned about the strange sense of fear which was seething within her heart.

2

As Laura stood almost rooted beside the burning bus, searching frantically with her eyes for her missing baby, she understood finally what she had been feeling. It had been a premonition, a warning. Somehow the Lord had tried to warn her . . .

Now she saw Ray, who was beating out flames on his badly burned clothing.

"Ray," she shrieked, her heart full of a hope which was somehow empty and hollow. "Where have you put Krystal?"

Hearing Laura's screams, Ray looked up, and Laura saw the blood drain instantly from his face. And then she knew with a certainty that was as cold as death, Ray had not been aware that Krystal was missing!

Abruptly his expression changed to one of such horror and disbelief that Laura could hardly endure it.

"Ray . . . ?" she questioned pleadingly. "Ray?"

"I . . . I . . . thought . . ." He stammered in shock. "Wasn't she with . . . with you?"

"Get her out of there!" Laura screamed. "Get my baby out of the camper!"

With a bleak look on his grimy face, Ray turned and leaped through the door of the bus, vanishing into the fire. By this time flames were billowing out of every window, and the entire bus was like a huge burning ball. Laura focused her eyes on the window by the bed where she had last seen Krystal.

In her mind Laura could vividly see the inside of the camper, a former school bus painted blue and converted into a motor home and known simply as *the bus*. The conversion job had been done professionally, with the kitchen area built along one side toward the front. It contained cupboards, a sink, a stove, and a refrigerator. Directly across from the kitchen, taking up the same amount of space along the far side, was a small bed. It was about three and a half feet above the floor and had always made an excellent place for Krystal to play while Laura was cooking. That was where Laura had last seen her baby.

Now, as she saw the flames leaping out of the window above that little bed, Laura knew that no one could possibly live through such terrible heat. "Please!" she heard herself sobbing over and over, "Please, someone, help my baby! Help me . . . please . . . !"

"Thank you, Tami," Laura gasped, as she lifted an armload of blankets from her thirteen-year-old daughter's slender arms. "I don't know how I'd ever make it without your help."

It was Saturday, and at last they were loading the bus, nearly ready to leave for their camping trip. Laura's feelings of foreboding had vanished, and with a great sense of relief she was looking forward to spending the weekend with her parents.

"That's okay, Mom," Tami replied happily. "After I feed Pungo I'll get Krystal. Then you won't need to worry about either of us. We'll both be—"

"Mom," eight-year-old Shelli interrupted, "let *me* get Krystal. It's my turn, and I don't—"

"Shelli," Tami retorted, "why do you always—?"

"Ladies," Laura interposed, smiling at her two daughters.

"Krystal has plenty of love for everyone. We don't need to divide her up. Tami, you get Krystal and bring her to the bus. Shelli, I want you to get her coat and the extra box of Pampers."

"Aw, Mom," Shelli wailed, "I—"

"Hold it, all of you!" Ray called from the front of the bus. "There's no point in arguing over which of you gets Krystal. I already have her, right here, and she's going to help me drive. In fact, we're ready to leave, so if any of the rest of you are coming along, you'd better hustle."

Gratefully Laura smiled at her husband, who grinned, winked at her, and then said sternly so that his girls would hear, "That means you, too, Laura. Get a move on!"

Laura pulled a shocked face and marched stiffly past her husband and out of the door; the girls giggled and followed her; and Krystal, in her father's lap, made little motor noises as she tugged at the steering wheel. It was obvious to all of them that Krystal was in a hurry to get going.

"Mom!" Kari suddenly called out from the house as Laura stepped from the bus. "Something smells in here! Something's burning!"

"The bread!" Laura gasped. "I forgot the bread!"

Hastily she ran for the house, the smell of burning bread telling her that she had indeed forgotten . . .

As the stench from the burning bus assailed Laura's nostrils and as the heat battered against her face, her frantic thoughts fled again to memories of her family. It was almost as though her mind was doing its best to shut out the horrible scene before her. But the memory the scene sparked was not a good one, and Laura felt her chest restrict and her muscles tense with fear, for she was experiencing another fire, another terror.

Three-year-old Kari Lyn had been standing in her flannel nightgown against a heater. Apparently the heater had malfunctioned, for a tiny flame leaped out, igniting the child's clothing.

Laura, in another room, heard her daughter's screams and in a sort of vision she saw Kari engulfed in flames. Racing through the house to Kari, Laura threw her to the floor, lay on top of her, and smothered the flames with her own hands and body.

Then, just two years later, an accident caused by the family cat had burned their home to the ground. No one was injured, though Shelli had been endangered for a while. But the family lost everything, and the whole thing was a terrible ordeal.

"Why?" Laura shouted suddenly, "Why is it always fire? Why do my babies . . . ?" _____

Laura was standing at the sink in her large and airy kitchen, finishing the last of the breakfast dishes. Her babies, Jenni and Krystal, were seated in the rocking chair in the living room, playing contentedly with their dolls.

Krystal loved dolls, especially her Sesame Street characters. Laura had watched her play with them for hours. None of the other girls had so enjoyed dolls at such an early age, yet Krystal did, and . . .

"Mommy," Jenni yelled, holding her doll up in the air. "Look! Krystal's doll is a baby, and mine is an old mommy, just like you are."

Laura smiled at her, turned away, and almost giggled as she thought of what Jennifer had said. It was a classic statement, one that needed to be recorded for the future. Someday Jenni would laugh over it, and maybe even feel a tinge of embarrassment.

The trouble was, the statement was also partially true. Laura was an entirely different person to her children than she was to herself.

"My word!" she exclaimed aloud. "I don't feel any different than I felt the day I got out of high school. Yet to the kids I'm as old as Methuselah. And to them I must look it, too. After all, Ray did find another gray hair this morning. How terrible, to be only thirty-four, to have six children, and to be going gray. Maybe—"

"Mommy," Krystal shouted, interrupting Laura's solo conversation, "nummy-nummies, okay? Want nummy-nummies for baby."

Laura smiled and handed her youngest a slice of fresh peach, and as the little girl marched proudly back to the rocker, Laura reflected on the problems she and Ray had encountered in trying to get Krystal and Jennifer into their family.

One miscarriage had followed another until, in desperation, she had knelt down one day, poured out her soul to her Heavenly Father, and pleaded with him to allow her to have two more babies.

"Why two?" Ray asked when she told him of her prayer.

"I don't know," Laura replied in a serious tone. "It's just that I have always felt, ever since I was a little girl, that I would have six children. Ray, I still feel that way. If I'm right and if we exercise enough faith, Heavenly Father will send us two more. I know he will."

Laura smiled as she recalled Ray's look of perplexed disbelief. And yet, in that same look, she had seen total love and total support. Ray may not always have understood how she felt, but he always loved and he always trusted. And that was why, even as she stood with her hands in dirty dishwater, Laura felt herself tingling as she thought of how much she loved her husband.

He was such a good man. He was quiet, yet he was solid and deep. He was even becoming more vocal as the years passed, and now that he was on the city council and in the elders quorum presidency, people paid attention when he spoke. And they *should* pay attention, she felt, for as Laura had learned, Ray was a man of unusual wisdom and sensitivity.

At that moment, for no good reason except that she loved her husband, Laura's eyes filled with tears. She was doing her best to wipe them with her one dry arm when . . . when . . .

The muffled explosion rocked the burning bus gently back and forth, and Laura realized that she had not seen Ray come back. But he must have! It had been such a long time since he had gone inside! How could he still be in there? How could he possibly endure . . . ?

And did he have Krystal yet? He *must* have her, though! She could not doubt that. She must not doubt it. He had to find . . .

"Oh, dear God," she sobbed, wiping at her streaming tears with her forearm, "please get Ray and Krystal out of there. Please . . . please . . . it has been too long, and . . . ."

"Ray! Oh, Ray, where are . . . ?"

Now, for the first time, Laura became conscious of the other people in the campground, people who were even then running toward her. But they were coming so slowly, so slowly, almost as though they were moving in a slow-motion picture.

They would never make it. She knew that! They would never get there in time to help Ray, to help Krystal! Oh, was there no one. . . ?

From the bus came the unmistakable sound of shattering glass, a window which had exploded. It sounded almost like a dish dropping, yes, a dish . . .

"Oh, Krystal!" Laura's voice was filled with impatience. "I told you to hold it carefully. Now you've broken Mommy's pretty dish. I . . . ."

But as Laura noticed the look of total dejection on her tiny daughter's face, her irritation vanished.

"Oh, sweetheart," she said softly, gathering her baby into her arms. "That's okay. Mommy knows you didn't mean to break the dish. Here, give me kisses. Mmmmmmmm, that's a sweet little girl. There! Run along now, Krystal, so Mommy can get the peaches bottled. We can't go see Grandma and Grandpa until they're finished."

As Krystal ran outside, Laura quickly swept up the broken pieces and finished the dishes. Then, still hurrying, she vigorously attacked the bushels of peaches which were stacked on the back porch.

Out of her kitchen window she could see the Book Cliffs, now a hazy blue and ochre in the heat of the desert day. They were a vivid contrast to the cool green of the alfalfa fields which stretched out from the back of her home. Yet even over those the heat waves were shimmering, giving the illusion of vast acres of water, water that was in reality nothing more than arid desert.

Mountains. The view caused Laura to think of her father, a wonderful man who loved the mountains but who had not yet seen the necessity of worshiping, at least formally, the creator of them. Laura had a difficult time understanding her father's Church inactivity, but that didn't change her love for him at all. He and her mother were two of the greatest people Laura had ever known. Still, all her life she had longed for them to strengthen their testimony of the gospel. If only they could see . . .

But as yet they *hadn't* seen, despite Laura's patriarchal blessing. In that blessing a promise had been made to her that if she would be faithful and if she would endure great personal sacrifices without murmuring, then one day she would be able to work in the temples of the Lord with her parents.

She wasn't certain what that meant, but it seemed to be saying that through her own personal sacrifices she could bring the great blessing of Church activity into the lives of her parents. That was an exciting promise, for Laura loved her parents dearly. Yet it was also a frightening promise, for each time she thought of the phrase "great personal sacrifice," she thought of the possible death of one or more of her children. With that thought, of course, came a chill of fear, for she could think of nothing that would be a greater sacrifice than losing her children.

Laura had even gone through each of the six in her mind, trying to determine which child she could let go most easily. The answer, obviously, was none of them.

Another question, however, gave a far different answer. Sometimes Laura would ask herself which of the children was most ready to go. The answers, of course, were her babies, Jenni and Krystal. And every time she thought of that, her mind seemed to center on Krystal, and a cold hand of terror would grip her heart. How, oh, how could she ever bear the pain of parting with her darling baby?

Could it be possible that Krystal was too good, too special, too pure, to remain on the earth? Was that why Laura always thought of Krystal when she thought of one of her babies dying? Was Heavenly Father going to take her smallest child away? Was Krystal . . . ?

"Mom?" Tami suddenly asked, her voice sounding tiny and distant in the roar from the fire. "Is Krystal going to die?"

Spinning around, Laura grabbed her oldest daughter by the shoulders and shook her.

"No!" she shouted. "No! Don't say that! Don't say it ever. Krystal is fine. Krystal is . . ."

And then, dissolving into tears, Laura threw her arms around her daughter and wept, almost unaware at first that the other children were gathered around, each of them also wondering, each of them concerned about Krystal.

As Laura grew conscious of their presence and as she thought of the task of explaining to them what must surely be true, her tortured mind recoiled, and once again she moved into a different time, a different place.

The hot afternoon was filled with fruit and interruptions, and Laura was certain she would not get everything done before they were to leave for Joe's Valley. And frankly, she told herself, it would serve her right for trying. There was not really time for a weekend camping trip anyway. Yet her parents had invited them, and because the children needed time with their grandparents and because they all needed a break, they had decided to go.

But before she knew it school was out, and the children were home from their first week of the new school year, bringing more interruptions. Scott was all full of enthusiasm about the beginning football season and the team's prospects for glory. Tami, for once not on her horse, was all a flutter about some boy in the ninth grade. But then Shelli, who very much idolized her eldest sister, appeared in Tami's lipstick, doing her best to imitate her.

Laura thought the ensuing battle would be heard all the way into town, and she quickly brought it to a halt. Stooping, she picked up Krystal, carried her over, and placed her in Tami's arms. Then quickly, before Shelli could move, Laura grabbed her little arms and wound them around Krystal and Tami. Krystal, in the middle, did exactly as Laura had known she would. She put her arms around both of her sisters, smiled, and then grabbed at their ears. In spite of themselves, both Tami and Shelli burst out laughing, and the fight was over.

"Remember, you two," Laura said gently, "Krystal was the last of you to be with Heavenly Father, and her spirit is still the spirit of peace. That's the way Heavenly Father wants both of you to be. Now repent, and let's get on about your lives."

Finally, as Laura turned back to the sink, she caught sight of Scott, who was quietly leaving the kitchen. She smiled. How effectively her only son avoided the feminine conflicts which regularly surged around him. Somehow she had to find a way to tell him how much she loved and appreciated him. He was twelve, the age when hugs and kisses were worse than curses, so it would need to be some way other than that. Maybe if she—

"Mommy!" Krystal was tugging at Laura's dress. "Mommy, see!"

Startled that her youngest daughter had crept up on her so quietly, Laura looked down to see Krystal standing close to her while Shelli stood in the doorway giggling mischievously. Then, catching sight of Krystal's tiny outstretched hand, Laura gasped in disbelief.

"See, Mommy!" Krystal said excitedly, lifting her hand even closer to her mother's shocked face. "Pretty!"

Unable to decide whether to laugh or to scream, Laura found herself eyeball to eyeball with what appeared to be the world's largest black stinkbug, a stinkbug which was, at that very moment, doing its unlevel best to raise its perfumed end to new heights in the world of scent.

Laura decided to scream.

3

Still screaming, Laura stood transfixed with horror as the bus rocked back and forth with a new explosion. Flames now were shooting fifty feet into the air, and as she felt her skin tightening with the heat she stepped involuntarily backward, once, and then again.

"Ray!" she screamed. "Ray, where are you?"

And then, all at once, he was there, stumbling toward her, his clothing burning again and his face a mixture of black and bright red.

"I . . . I can't . . . get in from the front," he coughed. "I'll . . . try the back!"

"I'm going in, then!" Laura shrieked, and she sprinted toward the steps of the bus. "I won't wait! I can't!"

"Laura, no!" Ray shouted. "Don't do it! You'll never make it."

But Laura, beside herself with fear and agony, ignored the pleas of her husband. She had to try, she had to do something more than just stand and wait. Nevertheless, she was almost certain that she had waited too long already. If Krystal was dead, she would never forgive herself. Never!

The inside of the bus was a searing conflagration of red-hot terror, and Laura found that after only a few seconds of intense pain her eyes simply ceased to function. She could see nothing except the fury of a thousand hells as they roared around her.

Where was Krystal? How could she see her? And if she couldn't see, how could she possibly find her?

"Krystal! Krystal, where . . . are . . . ?"

"Jenni, if you're going to help me babysit Krystal you've got to pay more attention. Do you know where I found her?"

Jenni shook her head back and forth, her eyes downcast.

"In the middle of the road, Jenni, almost to the canal."

"I'm sorry, Mommy. She snucked away, and I didn't see her go."

Laura knelt down and took her daughter's hands into her own.

"I know she did, Jenni. Krystal likes to wander, and I lose her too. All of us do, unless we pay attention. But Krystal is still a baby, Jenni, and she doesn't know how to take care of herself. That's why I need you to help me watch her. Together we'll—Krystal? Krystal, where *are* you? Honestly, that child! Come on, Jenni. Now she's gotten away from *me*. Let's find her together."

Now, holding her arms before her face and ducking her head to protect her eyes, Laura plunged further into the roaring inferno in search of her daughter. But she was only able to stumble forward for perhaps five or six feet before she could physically go no further. There was no air to breathe, and the intensity of the heat made her entire body feel as though it was being destroyed.

"Krystal! Krystal!"

But there was no sign of the baby, no indication that she was anywhere near. Nor could Laura hear anything above the constant roaring of the flames.

"Please, Krystal? Where are you?"

Now Laura's mind filled with the realization that her dear little baby was dead, and that she could do nothing about it, and that she herself was burning. Gagging with sudden nausea, she turned and groped her way back out of the bus, her clothing and hair on fire and her heart breaking with the certainty that her baby was being consumed by the flames.

As close to hysteria then as she had ever been, Laura did not even notice that people, other campers and her own family, were beating out the flames that were still leaping from her own clothing. She simply staggered away from the bus, enshrouded in total despair and agony.

Then she saw her father, ran to him, and felt his grief-stricken frame embrace her.

"Oh, Daddy," she sobbed, "she's gone! She's gone! Daddy, I would never have left the bus if I had known that Ray didn't have my Krystal! Daddy, I hurt so bad . . ."

"Now, Laura," her father said as he gently held her small trembling body close to him. "You're not hurt badly, you're only scared. The bike is okay too, so you have nothing to worry about. Now, come on, get up here on the seat and let's try it again. You can almost ride it."

Laura looked over at the new bike which her father had brought home for her, a new bike which was not new but only newly painted, and she felt a rush of affection for the large man who was holding her close. Oh, how she loved her daddy, how she loved having him hold her! But he did it so rarely. When he did, though, Laura felt such a sense of security that she could not even describe it. If only she could explain it to him! Perhaps then he would understand and would hold her close to him more often. It helped so much . . . so much . . .

Before her father could speak, Laura wrenched free from his embrace and ran back to the bus. In actual time it had been only a few minutes since the first explosion, yet to Laura it seemed hours. The fire was awesome in its size, and as she stared at it she cried out, "How can I endure this? Dear God, how can I stand it? I am here alive, in one piece, my darling baby is in there being burned alive . . . and I can do nothing. Oh, dear Father, why? Please tell me *why?"*

"Why, Daddy? Huh? Why can't we stay until Tuesday?"

Shelli had come to the front of the bus and was standing by the driver's seat looking earnestly up into her father's face.

"Please, Daddy," she repeated. "Let's stay until Tuesday. Okay? Grandma and Grandpa won't mind, and you can get more fishing in."

"Laura," Ray called, "do something with this kid, will you? She's lost her memory someplace and can't seem to remember that she has school next Tuesday."

"But Daddy," Shelli groaned, "*lots* of kids miss school. All the time, too. We only want to miss one day. Just this once, please? We won't ever ask you again. Honest we won't. Please?"

"Come on, Shelli," Laura laughed, "let's go sit down and I'll tell you a story."

"Hey, Mom," Kari called from the back of the bus, "come on! We're playing the alphabet game, and you get to be on Jenni's side."

Laura rolled her eyes at Ray in mock dismay, took Kari by the hand, and walked back to sit with Jenni. For the next couple of hours, the whole family played car games. When the children grew tired of that, they joined in singing and in telling stories.

Finally, when they were all in a silly mood, they got to the jokes. As they recited them one after another, everyone roared with laughter. Laura knew, even as her side ached, that she wasn't laughing because the jokes were particularly funny, or even because they were new. In fact, they were neither. It was just that all of them, especially her, needed to relax. And she *was* relaxing, with all of her heart and soul.

At last, when no one could think of another joke, Ray told the kids that a five-dollar bill would be the prize for the last game. All got excited and ready—all, that is, except Tami, who sat watching her younger brothers and sisters with total disgust spread across her face. As she drummed her fingers with impatience, Ray told the rest of the children that the five dollars would go to the first person who saw a duck-billed platypus crossing the highway.

The groans (except from Jenni, who wanted to know what a . . . a . . . whatever-it-was was) were immediate and in unison. "Come on, Daddy," they echoed derisively.

"Sponges," Tami said sarcastically, while both Laura and Ray grinned. "When are you going to learn to ignore Daddy? He's not going to give away a five-dollar bill! We can't afford . . ."

"Mommy," Shelli asked with childlike frankness as she stood hiding behind her mother's legs, "can Daddy afford to have our bus burn up?"

"Shelli," Tami responded, her voice full of shock and indignation, "who cares about the dumb old bus? Krystal is in there dying, and she's the one we ought to be worrying about. Now stop bugging mother with such dumb—"

"Tami." Laura interrupted her oldest daughter. "It's all right. She's asking normal questions for someone her age." She turned to Shelli. "No, Shelli, we can't afford it. But it's only money, and we'll get that back someday. But Krystal . . . !"

Laura gazed out of the window at the magic serenity of the mountains. Darkness was fast approaching, and the bus was finally moving up out of the desert. The aroma of sagebrush filled the air, and the hills were dark with thick stands of juniper—cedar trees, she had always called them.

Laura loved the smell of the mountains and the feeling of peace she normally felt when she was there. Yet now there was no peace, no enjoyment of the cool and fragrant air. The sense of foreboding was back, and she could not understand it.

Was it that they were going to have an accident? Could that be the cause of her worries? If Ray lost control of the bus on the steep and winding road, and if it rolled and caught fire, could she get her family out? And something else—if the bus did roll and burn, who would be most likely to get hurt?

Laura's thoughts centered instantly around Krystal, and again she felt the cold hand of terror clutching at her chest. Not her baby! She was so young and so helpless!

With that dread possibility in mind, Laura felt that she must stay near Krystal, in case she needed help. She was her mother, and Krystal was her responsibility. Instinctively Laura reached out for the child. She wanted her close, in her arms, where she could protect her.

But Scott had other ideas. He too wanted to hold his little sister, and he coaxed and pleaded until Laura gave in.

Happily Scott picked Krystal up and carried her to his seat. For some time he held her on his lap, teasing her and pulling grotesque faces at her. This delighted Krystal, who swung her tiny uplifted hands toward him, returning his play to the best of her ability. She would grab Scott's ears and give them a quick jerk, bringing forth a howl of mock pain from her brother. Delighted with what she had done, Krystal would throw her head back in laughter, and then the whole process would begin again.

Laura, had she tried, would not have been able to find words to describe how much she loved and enjoyed her family. She and Ray had talked about it and had concluded that their marriage seemed to be increasing in joy and harmony largely because the children were happy and content with each other. And they were, almost constantly. In fact, Krystal's birth had seemed to mark the beginning of an increase of love and harmony among the children.

Now, as Laura watched Krystal and Scott playing, she felt once again that her youngest baby had been a precious gift to the family. Each of the children felt toward Krystal as Scott did, and each of them constantly searched her out to play with her. They all delighted in her presence, and each of them, at one time or another, had told Laura that they had a special feeling about their baby sister. She was like an angel of peace to the family, and all of them sensed it.

With those thoughts came the nagging, foreboding feeling that Laura had been fighting, and once again she was almost overcome with despair.

"Heavenly Father," she pleaded, "help me to understand why I am feeling this way. Something awful is going to happen, I *know* it is! And yet I feel so helpless, so lonely, so empty . . . What can I do?'

Laura stood helplessly watching the bus burn, her heart aching, her soul empty and hollow, her mind a place of rushing thoughts —questions and feelings which she could hardly understand, let alone cope with. Yet they were there, and she was not able to cast them from her mind.

"The fire is so fierce," she thought. "Surely there won't be anything left of Krystal when it's been put out. Has anyone phoned for help? Has anyone found a way to notify a fire department somewhere? Maybe when they come I can go inside and look for my baby.

"Oh, Krystal, did you look for me and I wasn't there? Maybe you saw me going down the hall with Kari. Did you try to follow? Did you crawl down the hall after me, calling 'Mommy, Mommy!' I would never have left the bus if I had known that you were still inside, my little darling. I hope that you know that. I have never let you out of my sight. I have never gone anywhere without you. I have done everything I could think of to protect you. Oh, how could I have let this happen to you? You were my responsibility, not Ray's. I am your mother, and it is my sacred duty to look after you. Heavenly Father gave you to me and trusted me with you. Oh, Krystal, how could I have let this happen?

"How could I let you suffer and die in such a horrible way? My dear little Krystal, please forgive me? Please, *please* forgive me!"

For a few seconds Laura stood, totally empty, just staring at the bus. Then, because there was no where else to turn, she dropped her head and turned to the Lord.

"Heavenly Father," she sobbed, "if Krystal is gone, please help me to know, to understand why. Help me to accept this . . . this tragedy graciously, and comfort all of us . . . please! I . . . Oh, dear God, I don't think I can stand this! Please tell me that it is a nightmare, before I go crazy."

For an instant there, Laura had the impression that Krystal was indeed dead; further, that her death was not accidental but part of an eternal plan.

Yet . . . yet . . . her mind could not accept what she felt, and immediately the questions began. If she had known of an eternal plan, if her premonitions had been correct, then why hadn't she been able to prepare for it? Why hadn't she been able to save her little daughter? Surely she could have rescued Krystal if she had had the courage to go through the fire. Krystal's death had been her fault; she had been responsible for it and she would carry the guilt of it to. . . .

Suddenly Laura was aware that an arm was around her waist. Looking up, she saw that it was Ray, standing looking at her, tear of grief streaming down his face.

"Laura," he said brokenly, "I . . . I'm . . . sorry. I couldn't find her . . ." And Ray buried his face against his wife's neck and wept. Great sobs wracked his charred and bleeding body, choking sobs that seemed to tear him apart. Laura, with her arms around him, wept too, wept with an aching which she couldn't yet even begin to comprehend.

"No!" she cried in anguish. "No! No! No! Oh, please, God, not yet! Not already! She's too young, too . . . Oh, nooooo! Don't forsake us now!"

"Honey," Ray said after a minute or so of silence, "don't talk like that. It isn't like you. The Lord isn't forsaking us. He wouldn't, especially when *you* try so hard to be righteous. Painful as it is, this must be the best thing. Somehow we have to trust him."

"Do you mean," Scott asked, "that we have to go to church, even while we're camping?"

"Of course, dear," Laura replied. "Just because we're away from home, that doesn't mean that Heavenly Father stops being our Heavenly Father. We expect him to bless us all the time, so we ought to obey him all the time, even here. Don't you agree?"

"Yeah, I guess so. But—"

"No buts, Scott. Heavenly Father has asked us to go to church, so we trust him and we go. If we didn't trust him, then we really wouldn't even believe in him, would we? Now, let's hurry, or we'll be late."

Laura and her family spent all of Sunday in the community where her parents lived, attending meetings and visiting with members of the family. Everyone seemed happy, and Laura could not remember when she had enjoyed herself more. Her bad feelings were gone, the children were well behaved and pleasant, and Krystal was everywhere, delighting everyone with her presence. Once again Laura breathed a prayer of gratitude for her children.

"Ray," she said, as they drove toward the chapel, "I can't tell you how good it feels to feel good."

"That makes a whole lot of sense, Laura. It really does."

"Come on, Ray. You know what I mean."

"Oh, I know what you mean, honey," Ray said, grinning. "It's just that I'm not sure if *you* meant to mean what you said when you meant to say what you meant to mean when you said it."

"What? But I don't . . . Oh, I get it! Ha-ha! You're not very funny, you know."

"Well, what's one opinion out of millions?"

"Be serious, Ray, will you? I'm trying to tell you that it is such a relief to be freed from that terrible, oppressive sense of disaster. I want to sing, to shout out, to tell everyone how happy I feel. I want to tell them how delightfully marvelous everything is."

"My goodness, but you *are* in a good mood."

"I certainly am, Ray."

"Well, do me a favor, honey. If you decide to sing and shout and so on, wait until we get back into the mountains. They have an ordinance here against noise pollution, and the kids and I value our freedom."

"Oooh, you big . . . big . . ."

"Uh-uh-uh. This is Sunday, my dear eternal companion. Watch your language."

They both laughed then, and the children, who had been listening, eagerly joined in. Even Krystal, who obviously understood little of what was going on, took part in the joyous mood of the family.

In fact, the eighteen-month-old girl was her happy angelic self until shortly after the worship service had begun. Then she became restless, and soon she grew so noisy that Laura finally asked Shelli to take her out. The two little girls spent the remainder of the service playing on the lawn in the front of the meetinghouse, waiting happily for their family to come out and join them.

That night, back on the mountain, Krystal cuddled in Laura's arms, nursing, and grinned happily up at her. Finally, when she was finished, she played for a few moments and fell asleep, safe and secure in the embrace of her mother.

Gazing down at her baby, Laura realized more than ever how much she loved her sleeping, blond-headed, dark-eyed angel. What a joy Krystal's special spirit was to her! Hundreds of times she had held her baby just so, nursing, and she never tired of it. Of course, there were some who questioned the wisdom of nursing for so long, but let them question. For her and her babies it had been right, and she wouldn't change it for anything.

"Dear Heavenly Father," she prayed silently, as she gazed at her little daughter, "thank you so much for this sweet spirit, this little angel who has graced the lives of each of us. Bless her, please, and protect her for me. Help me to always be the kind of mother she and the other children will be proud of."

"Laura, honey," Ray said, still struggling with his voice. "We've got to be strong for the children. We're the only ones who can show them how to react to this tragedy. Now, come and help me. I know what we have to do, and without your support I can't do it."

Through their tears the two of them looked at each other for a long moment, drawing strength from each other. At last, hand in hand, Ray and Laura gathered their remaining five children together and led them to the top of a small hill that was nearby. As they all kneeled with hands joined together, Laura wept again as she listened to her dear husband pour out his agony and grief to his Heavenly Father. He pleaded for understanding, and through more tears he pleaded for strength not only for himself but for his entire family, that each of them might be able to endure the loss of their beloved little Krystal.

And bless them the Lord did—immediately. Almost instantly

Laura felt herself suffused with new strength, as though a blanket of energy had been wrapped around her body. With that strength, which she knew was not her own, she was able to rise and to minister to the needs of her family.

Carefully and gently, feeling almost as though she was another person, she moved among her children, loving them, caressing them, and comforting them. Never could she remember feeling so at peace. Filled with that spirit she spoke to each of the children, telling them one at a time, in a way that each could understand, that everything was all right. Krystal, she explained, had gone back to live with Heavenly Father, and though she was missing them as much as they were missing her, she was happy in her new home. They all needed to be happy for her as well. They *could* be happy, too, Laura told them, for the Holy Ghost would comfort them, as he was comforting her and the children's father, and they would be at peace.

"Mommy," Kari said, as Laura hugged her, "I miss Krystal so badly. Our family feels empty without her."

"Yes it does, Kari. We all miss her. But maybe, if we are righteous, Heavenly Father will let her visit in our family occasionally. Would you like that?"

"Oh, yes! Mommy, could we see her?"

"I don't know, sweetheart. I suppose that would be up to Heavenly Father."

"Well, I don't guess it really matters, does it? Besides, Mommy, if she's with Heavenly Father, then we don't have to worry about her anymore, do we? She won't wander away from him, will she?"

"No, Kari, she won't. She'll be contented there, and we must try to be the same here . . ."

And then the tears came anew, and Laura could no longer continue.

TWO

4

The bus had been burning for over an hour before Laura saw the first outside help arrive, a county sheriff. A short time later an ambulance and a fire truck pulled up, and the firemen immediately set about containing the fire.

Since the prayer, Laura had been able to deal with the tragedy largely because of the Holy Ghost, who seemed to have erased all negative emotions from her mind. But the sheriff, in the course of his on-the-site investigation, was forced to ask questions. Those questions, innocently pursued, brought all the guilt and loneliness back into Laura's consciousness, and she found herself once more almost devastated.

"Ray," she pleaded, "do we *have* to do this? I mean, right now?"

"Yes, honey, I guess we do. The sheriff has to file a report about how Krystal . . . died. I . . . I'm sorry . . . about this. Anyway, he can only do that if we try to tell him what happened."

"But Ray, I don't know if I can do it."

"You can, honey. I'm struggling too, but we'll all do it together."

"Ma'am," the sheriff added, "I'll hurry, and don't worry if there is something you can't talk about. The last thing on earth I want to do is hurt you more than you've already been hurt. Do you think you can help me?"

After a moment Laura silently nodded; and gradually, with bits and pieces of information added by each of the family members, the story of Krystal's death began to unfold.

Laura started, and speaking quietly she told what she remembered of the morning. For her, the tranquility of Joe's Valley had first been shattered when Ray and four of the children arose and departed for the reservoir, where they would join Laura's parents for the first fishing of the trip. Tami and Krystal somehow managed to sleep through the racket, and when the door to the bus finally closed for the last time Laura herself rolled over and, with Krystal in her arms, went back to sleep.

Later the three of them awakened, and Laura and Tami dressed and were in the process of cooking breakfast when the excited, hungry fishermen returned. Shelli had caught her first fish, and she was noisily asking that her mother cook it immediately. The others were just as hungry but were willing to be satisfied with less exotic fare.

That morning Krystal was restless and hungry. She wanted her mother to hold her and was making quite a fuss about it. However, breakfast for the others was in the process of being cooked. Laura had only two hands, and so she placed Krystal on the bed across from the stove.

When the family filed in, Krystal's fussing was a prominent part of the atmosphere. Ray put Jenni on the bed beside her, and then he too sat there, both of them doing what they could to comfort the baby. But in Krystal's mind, neither of them would do. She was hungry, she wanted her mother, and that was that!

Another one of the children, feeling sorry for the baby, decided to climb onto the bed and help tend her. For a ladder the child used a small propane bottle which Ray had brought along for Laura's parents, but which had not yet been delivered. Somehow, as it was stepped on, the propane bottle was knocked over; the valve turned on, and the safety mechanism malfunctioned. Suddenly, liquid propane was spewing violently outward.

Laura instinctively stepped back from the spinning, spraying tank. Ray leaped to grab it, and as he did so it exploded. Instantly fire was everywhere, engulfing the bus.

With that part of the story told, Laura next described her escape with Kari Lyn from the rear of the camper, doing her best to control her emotions as she spoke of it. At that point Ray took over, and he recounted his and the childrens' involvement and efforts after the explosion.

When the propane bottle malfunctioned and began to spray, he told the sheriff, he, Jenni and Krystal had been on the bed. Shelli was nearby, Kari was behind her mother, and Tami and Scott were at the front of the bus, near the door.

As he leaped for the bottle, the liquid gas spraying from it hit the pilot light of the refrigerator and the whole area exploded. Tami and Scott were hurled out of the door, and Ray was thrown forward to a point where he rolled from the bus behind his oldest children, his clothing in flames.

Eight-year-old Shelli was also knocked forward, but when she clambered to her feet to escape, she heard screaming behind her. Turning, she saw Jenni standing in the midst of the flames crying. Without hesitation Shelli rushed to her little sister, grabbed her hand, and dragged her from the burning bus.

It was only seconds later when Laura appeared from behind the bus, and by then, though they tried, there was nothing more that any of them could do to save Krystal. They could only stand, watch, and feel the horror of the experience.

The sheriff made a few more notes about the abortive rescue efforts, commended Shelli for saving the life of her younger sister, expressed his appreciation and sympathy to the family, and left to join the firemen and the ambulance crew.

Within a short time the flames were extinguished, and not long after that the men began searching through the rubble for Krystal's body.

With all her heart Laura wanted to go into the bus, to aid in the search. Krystal was *her* baby, and she felt that if anyone had the right to look for and then to care for the little body, she did.

She knew only too well that Krystal's body would not look as it had when she had last seen her playing on the bed. She understood that her baby could not have lived through that terrible fire. No one could have survived such prolonged, intense heat. Still, she wanted to search.

"Ray," she said, "I'm going to go look for Krystal."

"Laura," her husband replied anxiously, "are you sure you should? I mean, do you think your emotions can handle seeing her the way she must look?"

"I don't know, Ray. I only know she's my baby, and I've got to find her."

Anxiously she spoke to one of the firemen, telling him that she wanted to find her baby and care for the body herself. In fact, she explained, she even wanted to take Krystal's body to the mortuary. After all, she had given birth to her and had cared for her in life, and she desperately wanted to do the same thing for her in death.

But the look of total horror which appeared on the man's face, and the comments made by others who were nearby, caused her to decide, contrary to her own feelings, to stay away from the search. Additionally, the fireman explained that he was required by law to give the body to the ambulance crew, and they were bound by the same law to deliver it to the mortuary. Legally, Laura could have no part in that process. Therefore it was best that she not push the matter any further.

Longingly she looked at the burned-out shell of the bus, yearning so much to see her baby for one last time. But . . . but she couldn't, not yet, and there wasn't anything she could do about it. So filled with new agony she turned away, allowing the men to proceed in their own way. Yet that decision would create unimaginable problems for her, and she felt certain at the time that she would live to regret it.

A part of her, of course, was grateful for the men's help. They were good men and were only following rules, doing their jobs. Yet another part of her, the mother part, resented their intrusion and their usurption of her right to care for her baby. Laura could not understand why they felt that they needed to do that, or why the laws of the land would force them to do it. To her, such thinking did not make sense.

Krystal's body was finally found, and then was placed in a body bag which was quickly carried to the ambulance. Moments later the ambulance driver approached Ray and Laura and explained to them, apologetically, that before he could leave he needed their signatures on several release forms.

Thoroughly exhausted emotionally, Laura sat numbly signing her name while the man explained in detail form after tedious form. "Please," she finally requested, "don't explain them all. I'm too tired to even think about what you're saying. Just show me where to sign, I'll do it, and we'll all be finished."

The man apologized and hurried her and Ray through the rest of the forms; Ray gave directions to the sheriff regarding disposal of the burned-out bus; and then the ambulance and the other official vehicles were gone, taking Krystal's body with them.

In spite of her requests, Laura had not been given even so much as a final glimpse of her beloved daughter's mortal remains. She was hurt deeply by that decision, and she was thoroughly frustrated that she could do nothing about it. Suddenly she found herself, with her family, alone on the mountain, alone with her grief and her emptiness. There was nothing left for them there, nothing at all. Krystal had been taken away, and there was no more for Ray and her to do but gather up the children and leave.

As they drove away, Laura felt more lost and more lonely than she had ever felt in her life. Why, she wept silently? Why, oh, why had it happened? Would she never understand? Would Heavenly Father never hear her cries and answer her?

That first endless night was spent in the home of Laura's parents. However, the family hadn't been there forty minutes before people began to arrive, friends and neighbors who came to express their sympathy and support.

Among the visitors were the home teachers of Laura's parents, two good men who understood the power of their callings. During their visit they gave priesthood blessings to each member of the family. Laura listened with gratitude as each child was promised that he or she would not suffer any mental or emotional trauma from the tragic event they had been a part of.

For Laura, however, the same promise seemed to have no effect. That night she was not able to sleep at all. Each time she closed her eyes she could see Krystal sitting on the bed in the camper reaching out to her, dressed in her little pink pajamas with the giraffes on them.

She knew Ray was also having trouble sleeping, since he was tossing and turning beside her.

"Ray," she finally said, her voice filled with anguish, "I don't think I can stand it. Please tell me all of this is a horrid dream, and that when I wake up it will all be over and Krystal will be back with me."

"Laura, I . . ."

"What did I do wrong, Ray? What did I do wrong? Is God punishing me because I'm a bad mother? I've tried not to be, you know that. I've done everything I could do to raise the children in righteousness."

"Honey, that isn't—"

"It's got to be the reason, Ray! Why else would Heavenly Father take her away from me? I've done everything I could do to be a good member of the Church. I've been morally clean, I've paid my tithing, I've attended my meetings regularly, I've sustained our leaders, I've never turned down a calling, and . . . and . . . Oh, Ray, I *wasn't* a good mother. I could have saved her, I know I could have! Oh, if only I hadn't been such a coward!"

"Ray," she continued brokenly, "did you see where they found Krystal's body?"

"Yes, Laura, I saw."

"She was in the hallway, Ray. She was crawling down the hallway, trying to reach me, trying to catch up with me. Ray, I left her behind! Don't you see that? In my cowardly hurry to save myself I left my baby behind to die, and now God is punishing me!"

Laura dissolved into tears, and her body began shaking uncontrollably as she sobbed. Gently Ray took her into his arms.

"Honey," he said quietly, "that simply isn't so. You did everything you could do. You easily did as much or more than I did. None of us could get to her—none of us!"

"Besides," he went on, "that bus was rocked by four separate explosions, any one of which could have thrown Krystal's body into the hallway. She wasn't following you. She couldn't have been. The fire was too sudden, too hot and too fierce.

"And Laura, you are not a bad mother! In fact, you're a wonderful mother, more caring and conscientious than any woman I've ever known. That's one of the reasons why I love you so much."

Though Laura's tears continued, her violent sobbing gradually diminished. As Ray gently stroked her hair she sensed that he was concerned about his inability to comfort her. Yet for some reason she could not help him by putting a stop to her crying. It was as though the strength given her that morning by the Holy Ghost was withdrawn and she was now alone, in pain, and with no place to turn for solace.

"Oh, Ray," she sobbed, "I hurt so bad! In every way imaginable I'm in pain."

"I know, honey. I . . ."

"No, you don't know!" Laura cried. "You *can't* know! You can't possibly understand what a mother feels! My milk came in hours ago, I have no one to nurse, and it hurts! Oh, how it hurts! Besides, I ache to hold her, yet my arms are empty, so totally empty that I don't think I can stand it! *Oh, where is my baby?* Ray, how am I going to survive without my Krystal?"

Much later, as Laura stared into the empty darkness, her thoughts returned to that morning in the bus, to the few moments when she had been busily preparing breakfast. Krystal had so much wanted to be held. She had cried and fussed, and Laura had told her no. If only she had picked her up! If she had, Krystal would be with her now, nursing, and the whole thing would be a bad dream, a terrible nightmare from which she would awaken. But she hadn't picked her daughter up, and it was no dream. It was real!

"Krystal," Laura said silently, as new tears coursed down her cheeks and into her pillow, "you must have wondered why I didn't pick you up and hold you this morning. Oh, my little darling, I did want to hold you. You must know that. I knew you were hungry, and I wanted to feed you. Only you had on those flannel pajamas, I was cooking over an open flame, and in my mind all I could see was Kari Lyn's nightgown burning as it did all those years ago. Krystal, I was afraid your clothing might catch on fire if you got too close to the stove. Oh, Krystal, please forgive me!"

5

When that first long night finally came to an end, Laura found that no one, not even the children, had slept well. They all ate breakfast with a generous neighbor, but their attempts to eat were at best a half-hearted effort. No one could make the food go down.

Borrowing Laura's parents' car, Ray drove the family to the mortuary. As Laura entered the silent building, the reality of Krystal's death was almost more than she could bear. Yet she was determined to maintain her dignity. If Krystal was watching them, Laura wondered, would she feel ashamed? More than anything, she wanted her little daughter to be proud of the way they were coping, so she resolved to carry herself in such a way that Krystal could not possibly feel otherwise.

First they were ushered into the mortician's office to make the funeral arrangements. There, for a brief time, Laura was able to forget her own grief as she felt her parents' and husband's sorrow. But the moment was fleeting, and it wasn't long before her mind had turned inward again, consumed with her own agony and loneliness.

From the office they were taken to a long narrow room filled with tiny caskets, where they were asked to choose one for Krystal. At the sight of the caskets Laura felt her knees begin to buckle, and it was all she could do not to turn around and run. But determinedly she forced herself to be calm, for she was certain that Krystal was watching.

Besides, she wanted Krystal's body to have a beautiful little "bed" in which it would repose as it awaited the resurrection, and it was her right to choose it. She could at least do that much for her baby. So after very little discussion the decision was made. The casket she and Ray chose was tiny, pink, and very feminine, the perfect resting-place for their baby daughter.

As they left the mortuary and began the long journey homeward, Laura sensed guiltily that for some reason she was emotionally withdrawing from the rest of her family. She did not want to do so, for she loved them with all her heart, and she understood that both Ray and the children needed her strength and support. Yet try as she would she could not wholeheartedly give it to them. She simply could not control the direction of her feelings. Krystal's death was all she could think about, and the horror of losing her and her own sense of guilt over it were the only emotions she could feel.

The drive across the desert to their home, which usually seemed so long, was much shorter that day. Laura could not stop thinking of the fact that she would be forced to enter the house without her baby, something she hadn't done since the day she brought her home from the hospital. Would she be able to do it, she wondered? Did she have the strength and courage to go through that doorway alone?

As they drove in gnawing silence, with no one speaking, Laura's thoughts leaped back to their trip to Joe's Valley. Everything had been so different before the accident. They had all been so happy, so full of life and excitement. What a contrast to their trip homeward!

And what of the people in their small community? Would it be hard to face them? Would those good people think it was her fault, or Ray's, that Krystal had died in the fire?

If only her friends would understand that they had tried to save her! If only they could look into Ray's heart, or into hers, and see the love for Krystal that each of them had! If they could, then surely neither she nor her husband would be blamed for Krystal's tragic death.

Ray had been so close to Krystal, much closer than he had been to any of the other children when they were babies. Often, Laura recalled, Ray had taken Krystal to town with him, or to his office. He had never even worried that she might wet a diaper, something that had been a real fear of his with each of the other children. Perhaps he too had sensed that Krystal's stay would be brief, so he had been doing all in his power to let his baby daughter know of his love.

Laura prayed fervently that their friends would know of and understand that love and would cast no blame upon them. She was already living with an agony of guilt that seemed beyond endurance, and Ray certainly felt the same. Could either of them survive some thoughtless soul's pointing finger of accusation?

Laura's worries were pointless, for by the time they arrived home, word of the tragedy had spread throughout town. Many friends had come to lend their support, and others had shown their love in a variety of ways. Their home had been thoroughly cleaned, dinner had been prepared, the yard had been raked, and the weeds in the garden had all been pulled.

As she became aware of all that her wonderful friends and neighbors had done, and as she thanked them personally, Laura began to warm, and some of the sorrow that had weighed so heavily upon her was lifted. The people had truly been unselfish and understanding, and she felt awful for having assumed that they would blame her for Krystal's death.

For a time Laura wandered from room to room, but every-where she turned, something reminded her of Krystal. The house seemed so empty without her! Laura found herself aching to hold her little daughter in her arms. She wanted to kiss her soft rosy cheeks and tell her how very much she loved her.

Yet as she looked at Krystal's small pink dress hanging emptily in the closet, the one she and Tami had sewn for the baby, she realized that the time for loving, for kissing, for dressing and for holding—that time was past. With trembling hands she lifted a rattle from the dresser, and in her mind she could see Krystal playing happily with it. As she fought back her tears she thought of the days when she had let the housework go so that she could hold her baby and sing lullabies to her. She thought too of the many hours spent in the rocking chair holding Krystal as she nursed, hours that might have been spent on her home or yard. How thankful she was that she had made decisions then which had allowed her to be with her daughter! Now there would be plenty of time for house and yard work, but there was no more time for holding or for loving her sweet little angel.

Looking up, Laura saw a framed poem hanging on the wall, the one given to her by a friend the day Krystal had created such a mess in the kitchen. She took it down and, wiping her eyes, she read:

> Sometimes you get discouraged
> Because I am so small
> And always leave my fingerprints
> On furniture and wall.
> But every day I'm growing,
> And soon I'll be so tall
> That all those little handprints
> Will be so hard to recall.
> So here's a special handprint,
> Just so you can say
> This is how my fingers looked
> When I placed them here today.

In an agony of loneliness and remorse, Laura turned the little handprint upside down and then opened a dresser drawer to put it out of sight. But her legs nearly gave way as she saw, on top of the neatly folded clothing, a photograph of Krystal.

44

"Oh Krystal," she cried in anguish, "it was my fault! I know it was! How could I have ever let such a terrible thing happen to you?"

Throwing herself onto the bed, Laura sobbed uncontrollably. She felt so lonely, so empty, so guilty, and so confused!

Why, she kept asking herself, did she feel so guilty? What was happening to her testimony? With every fiber of her being she knew that Krystal had died in perfect innocence, that she had gone back to the presence of God, and that her death must have been Heavenly Father's will.

With that kind of knowledge, and with the great faith in God's wisdom and love which she had always had, why did she feel so guilty about Krystal's death? For she did feel guilty. She did, and it did not make sense! If it had been God's will that Krystal die, then she could not have saved her. Yet if she had not stepped backward at the first stage of the explosion, but had stepped forward instead, she *could* have saved her. She knew that, for in her mind she could feel the explosion, she could see herself stepping backward from the stove, and she could see, through the flames, the outline of the bed where Krystal had been. It was so close . . . so close . . .

"Oh, Krystal," Laura sobbed, breaking down once more, "I'm so sorry. I don't know why I didn't step forward instead of backward. How I wish I had, for then I could have saved you. But I didn't, I didn't, and now . . . you're . . . gone . . . Oh, please forgive me . . ."

She cried out to God in her anguish of mind and soul. "Heavenly Father, why am I alive? Why isn't she? I've lived my life, known the joys of motherhood, the happiness of being a wife, a woman. Why can't my baby know those things? Why did she have to die in such a horrible manner? Why, oh why?

"It was because of me! I know it was because of me! What was it I did that caused her and me to deserve such punishments? Ray says that isn't right, Heavenly Father, that it isn't a punishment. But it must be! Such a thing is too awful to be anything else. Yet I don't know what I did. I just don't know! Please, dear God, help me to understand, help me to believe that it isn't a punishment, that I was not to blame . . ."

Finally Laura arose from the bed, cleaned herself up, and made her way into the kitchen. She was not really going anywhere, just wandering aimlessly . . . searching . . . searching . . . But on the cupboard in the kitchen was a plate of food, and attached to the plate was a letter. Absently Laura picked it up and began to read, and gradually she realized that the letter, from a friend who cared, was the inspired answer to her own tormented feelings and questions.

"Dear Ray and Laura:

"I just can't describe the overwhelming feeling of helplessness and sadness — we got back late Monday and got news of your Krystal and the tragedy of this weekend. Oh, how I wish there was something concrete we could do to help lift this burden from you, and ease the emptiness you and your family are going through!

"Eighteen joyous months with an angel child is such a short time to experience all the joys and emotions of a beautiful daughter. The Lord knows her worthiness, and now, during these last days of real trials and temptations, Krystal has her celestial inheritance, and Satan will never have an influence upon her. That blessing alone is wondrous — what a special daughter she is!

"Laura, we as mothers know of how close you have kept Krystal to you, never leaving her unattended, and of how careful you have been all through her short life. Not one of us can claim the same. You are a super mother, and Ray, you are a super father. How many comments I have heard this morning, all in praise of how great you both are as parents! The whole town echoes this feeling. All of us hope that you do not blame yourselves for what happened.

"Krystal loves you all and will watch each of you grow and return to her, and meanwhile she will fill an empty spot with grandparents and loved ones beyond the veil.

"Thank heavens for the gospel and for the sure knowledge which it gives to us. Your testimonies are strong — Heavenly Father knows that, and we do too. We love you."

Laura read the letter over several times, and each time she did so her soul felt a little more peace, a little more assurance. Her friends and neighbors did understand! Her prayers, for that at least, had been answered.

That night Laura and Ray knelt together beside their bed in prayer, and Ray's heartfelt words struck deeply into Laura's heart.

"Heavenly Father," he prayed, "help us to recognize that Krystal was your daughter before she was ours. Help us to realize in our hearts that you love her more than we do, and that you would never allow anything to happen to her that was not good. Please, Father, help us to understand that this . . . this . . . loss is not a terrible tragedy. Help us to see the good in it. Help us to see your love. Please . . ."

6

Wednesday, the day of Krystal's graveside service, dawned clear and dry. Laura watched with her heart in her throat as Ray, Scott, and her father left for the cemetery, where, after obtaining special permission, they would dig the grave. Ray, she sensed, felt as guilty about Krystal's death as she did and was anxious to find any way he could to show his daughter that he loved her and was sorry.

As Laura turned back to the kitchen, she thought of her husband and of the spiritual obstacles he had overcome in his life. As a boy, he had not been particularly involved in the Church. When he was a young man he had chosen the navy over a mission, and he and Laura had married civilly—she at eighteen, he at twenty-four.

Yet by then Ray's desire for an eternal inheritance was intense, and his entire life had become dedicated to learning obedience to his Heavenly Father. That was not easy for him, just as it was not easy for anyone else, Laura supposed. But Ray was tenacious and persistent, and just months after their marriage he had taken her through the temple.

Since that time he had continued to grow, and Laura knew that his faith was strong. He had had his trials—one of them being her, she supposed ruefully. But he had not complained. His parents had taught him to be self-reliant, had taught him that he alone was responsible for solving the problems and troubles that came his way. He did so, usually silently, and that was why Laura ached and prayed for him at this time. Krystal's death was all inside of him. He could not speak of it, could not share his grief over it, and thus he would allow no one to help ease his burden. Laura yearned to do so, but she felt at a loss as to how to proceed.

By the time they arrived at the cemetery the day had become scorching hot, the kind of weather known only to the desert. It was the kind of day, Laura recalled, that Krystal loved, the kind of day when she would play outside in the water. She wore a swimsuit when she had to, but when she could get away with it she enjoyed wearing much less.

As they drove along the narrow road that led to the cemetery, Laura considered for the first time how vast and lonesome it looked. How, she wondered, could she possibly leave her baby there?

The crowd at the cemetery was larger than Laura had expected, and its size helped to bolster her own faltering courage.

When she and Ray, followed by the children, approached the open grave, the people parted to let them through. As Laura felt the eyes of her friends and neighbors upon her, silently she began to plead again with the Lord, praying that both she and her husband would be able to carry themselves with dignity.

How she loved them, these people who had gathered to share their faith and spirit with her family! She did not want to make the experience any more difficult for them than it already was. She had to be strong—strong for her friends, strong for her father and mother, strong for her children. Especially she needed to be strong for Krystal, whom she felt certain was in attendance.

Laura thought again of her eternal sweetheart, the brave man who stood trembling at her side. Ray was to offer the dedicatory prayer over the grave, but he had expressed fear that he might not be able to say the things that were in his heart. Laura felt certain he could, and she had promised to stand by his side, to support him as he prayed.

"Heavenly Father," she pleaded silently, "bless Ray and me, please. Give us both the courage to be strong. Loose this dear man's tongue, Father, that he might say what he longs to say."

The mortician allowed Ray and Laura to carry Krystal's casket from the hearse to the grave. As they walked together, with their baby at last between them, a measure of peace filled Laura's heart. Finally, she thought, she was able to do something for her baby, the last thing she would ever do for her in mortality.

Following the opening prayer, a close friend sang "I Am a Child of God." Then came a short talk, given also by a good friend. Finally Ray arose and took Laura by the hand. Together they walked to the foot of Krystal's grave, where, trembling visibly, Ray offered the prayer.

As she tearfully listened, Laura knew that she was hearing the prayer of a man, a father, who had placed all his trust in a God whom he loved with his whole heart and soul. There was no bitterness there, nor anger. Though filled with loneliness and grief, it was a prayer of faith and, finally toward the end, hope.

It was a beautiful prayer, but the part that affected Laura the most, the thought that confirmed so much her own feelings, was the final thing Ray said. "Father," he pleaded, his voice quivering, "please ask Krystal to forgive us for . . . for what we allowed to happen to her."

As Laura listened to those words, the Holy Ghost bore witness to her, powerfully, that Krystal's death had been the will of the Lord. Even the manner of her dying had been part of a divine plan. She and Ray need not — should not — feel guilty.

Then a measure of peace, sweet, serene and pure, entered her heart, and Laura felt the love which God had for her, for Ray, for Krystal, and for each of his countless other children.

But to her surprise and disappointment, that feeling of peace did not remain with her. Instead, the days following the funeral were even more difficult than the time before had been. No matter how busy she kept herself with the mundane tasks of keeping up her home, Laura's thoughts turned repeatedly to Krystal, to the fire, and to what she considered her own ineptness in dealing with the moment of crisis. And the more she thought of that, the more she ignored the spiritual impressions she had received during the graveside service.

In fact, it became a vicious circle. Laura felt guilty about Krystal's death, and that in turn created more guilt—guilt over feeling guilty.

"Ray," she said one evening, "I don't know what to do. Sometimes I feel like I'm two separate people, and I don't think I can handle it any longer."

"Honey," Ray replied, looking perplexed, "you've lost me. I don't know what you're talking about."

"My guilt, Ray. I don't understand why I still feel so guilty. My testimony and the spiritual experiences we've shared tell me one thing, and yet all my natural inclinations tell me another. For some reason my mind won't accept what my heart keeps saying."

"Laura, I—"

"Please, Ray, let me finish. Every time my prayers are answered and I begin feeling a sense of peace, my mind goes back to that awful fire. There I am, not more than three feet away from where my baby is dying, and I do nothing! Just one more step, Ray, one more step, and she would have been in my arms, alive! I know that! I know it! And that's my problem. I can't overcome my guilt about Krystal's death, and I'm consumed with guilt because I can't. I'm between a rock and a hard spot, Ray. No matter which way I turn, I'm wrong."

"That's not true, Laura. Not really. All you have to do is stop talking about your guilt. Simply take it in your hands, mentally speaking, and throw it out of the window. Get rid of it. Once you quit talking about it, you'll quit thinking about it. When the thoughts are gone, so will be the guilt, and you can get on about your life."

At this, Laura felt tears welling up in her eyes, tears of pain and frustration.

"Ray, how can you ask me to stop thinking and talking about my baby? I could never do that! I—"

"Honey, listen to me. That isn't what I'm saying. I love Krystal deeply, and I'd never suggest that any of us forget her. We shouldn't, for she's an eternal part of us. But somehow we must remember her and at the same time forget the manner of her death. Until we do, I'm certain we'll continue to feel guilty about it."

"Is that what you've done, Ray? Can you honestly tell me you don't feel guilt anymore?"

"Of course I can't, Laura. I still feel guilty, terribly so! But I think I'm going in the right direction. You see, besides the guilt I also feel what the Spirit has whispered, and the Holy Ghost doesn't lie. I don't understand Krystal's death, Laura, but I'm a simple man, and I believe I should accept it. So should you."

"Sweetheart," Laura replied, her tears falling freely, "I know you're right. Only . . . for some reason my mind won't stop dwelling on this. I suppose it's like everything else in my life—I must know! I must have answers! I've always been that way. Being silent doesn't help me, Ray. I've got to talk about things, to think about them out loud until they become clear to me. If I don't, then it all starts to blow up inside of me, and I go to pieces. I've even prayed about it, constantly! I pray and pray and pray, and yet always Krystal is there, three feet away, dying because I don't reach for her. Oh, Ray, what am I going to do?"

"I don't know, honey," Ray said, as he drew his wife into his arms. "I see her too. And every time I do my emotions go to pieces, just like they are now. And that's pretty tough for a guy like me. But Laura, if together we exercise enough faith, then eventually Heavenly Father will make it easier for us. I know he will. That's the only answer we have left."

"Well, I hope he hurries, sweetheart," Laura replied, doing her best to smile. "I really do."

7

"Hey!" Ray shouted. "Cut that out!"

As the automobile sped down the highway Laura grabbed again at her husband's ribs, doing her best to tickle him.

"Laura, come on!" Ray gasped, grinning. "Do you want me to have a wreck?"

"If you do," Laura replied, smiling mischievously, "it won't be my fault. You don't drive this car any better than you drove that '55 Chevy you had when I met you."

"Wait a minute! I'm known far and wide for my safe driving."

"Oh, you are, are you? What about that night when you rolled your car into the river?"

"The river? I . . . oh, yeah! Listen, lady, I didn't roll it. It rolled itself. In fact, if you will recall, my dear, we were stopped, and you had my mind occupied with . . . uh . . . other things."

"Big deal! One or two little kisses, and you let the car roll into the river. Besides, we'd been married nearly a year."

"*Little* kisses! Good grief, Laura, that tells me a whole lot about your memory."

"There's nothing wrong with my memory, Ray."

"Well, then, there is with mine, Laura. And if there is, then maybe I'd better pull off the road for a few minutes. It's obviously time for a refresher course in your kissing technique."

"I'm sorry, sir," Laura said teasingly, "but I can't wait for you to stop. It's now or never."

Then, without waiting for a reply, and using her lipstick for ammunition, Laura made an assault against her husband's cheek, leaving a lasting impression as she did.

"Ah," Ray sighed, "how sweet it is! Laura, I just have one question."

"Yes?"

"What is it about me that's so irresistible?"

Without replying, Laura cuddled even closer, and for a time they rode in comfortable silence. But then Ray spoke.

"It sure feels good to relax and laugh a little."

"It really does, Ray. Yet I've just been sitting here feeling guilty again. How can I be laughing and having fun when I should be mourning our baby's death?"

"Hmmm. It's interesting that you would say that, honey. Sometimes I feel that way too. How about the fire? Are you still feeling that guilt as well?"

"Yes, Ray, I am. I keep wondering if I acted cowardly during the fire, or if perhaps my carelessness or neglect was the cause of Krystal's death. The other day I was reading in President Spencer W. Kimball's book on faith, and he said that people often die prematurely because of someone's carelessness. Ray, did my carelessness cause Krystal's death?"

"I don't know how to answer that, Laura."

"I have more questions, Ray, lots more. And I don't know how to find the answers. For instance, yesterday I was reading the book

Angel Children, and it quoted Joseph Smith as saying that if a person dies in childhood, and if its parents are righteous they will have the opportunity of rearing that child during the Millennium. Ray, if my carelessness caused Krystal's death, does that mean I forfeited my right to raise her? And even if I haven't lost that right, would Krystal *want* to be reared by a mother who allowed her to die? I don't know, Ray. I really don't know."

"Neither do I, Laura. As far as I know, all we can do is listen to the promptings of the Spirit."

"And another thing, Ray," Laura said, ignoring her husband's response, "I feel like I must know how much Krystal suffered. My mind won't rest until I do. I know that no one heard her cry out, and I can't understand that. Surely she would have screamed if she had been in pain."

"Think back for a minute, Laura. Do you remember when we gathered the kids together to pray, during the fire? You told me then that you had felt, even before you and Kari got out of the bus, that Krystal had already died. If your impressions were right, then Krystal would have had very little time to suffer . . . a few seconds, at most."

"But Ray, how could that be? None of the rest of us were even hurt. It just doesn't make sense!"

"I know it doesn't, Laura, and I don't know how to answer you. Maybe there isn't an answer. Maybe all we can do is exercise our faith and let it go at that."

There was nothing more that Laura could say, for she knew Ray was right. Yet . . . And then, suddenly, a thought came to her, a fleeting bit of memory that might be the answer to at least one of her questions.

As they had waited for the bus to stop burning, Laura recalled, Shelli had tried to talk to her, had tried to tell her about what she had seen of Krystal just before the explosion and fire. But Laura's mind had been too preoccupied with the demands of the ambulance driver, and she had paid no attention to her eight-year-old.

But Shelli had been there, as close to Krystal as anyone. She was even the one who had saved Jenni. Maybe she would know. Maybe . . .

"Choosing the headstone was pretty rough, wasn't it," Ray said.

Startled, Laura looked at him. "It really was," she agreed. "I hope Krystal likes it."

"She will. I liked the little poem you wrote, Laura. It will go well on the marker."

"Thank you, sweetheart. It . . . it just came to me."

For a few moments there was more silence, and then Ray spoke again.

"Laura, we've got to stop persecuting ourselves because of Krystal's death."

"Yes," Laura sighed, "I suppose we do. I've tried not to think about it, like you suggested, Ray. But I can't seem to help myself."

"I think I understand. I keep blaming myself too, even when I know I shouldn't. But, you know, Laura, I believe Satan wants us to feel guilt. It seems to me that when we're feeling guilty we're turned totally inward, only thinking of ourselves. To me that means being selfish, and I don't think being selfish is living the gospel."

Surprised, Laura looked at her husband. The headlights from an approaching car were illuminating his face, and she could tell he was serious. It was strange that she'd never thought of it that way before. The idea made sense, though. But what if she was unable to . . . ?

"Ray," Laura shouted excitedly, grabbing her husband's arm, "I know how I can get answers to all these questions! I'll ask Heavenly Father to let me see Krystal, visit with her. She's an adult spirit, and she could easily answer my questions."

"Whoa, honey! Wait a minute. I don't know if you have the right to ask to see her. I'm not sure you should *want* to. Besides, there must be other ways to get the answers."

"Not if I'm going to have peace, Ray. I've got to see her, to hear her tell me that she didn't suffer, that she doesn't blame me

56

for what happened. That's the only way my peace of mind will ever be restored."

"And if she doesn't come?"

"She will. I know she will. If I have enough faith, it can't be denied me. I've been tried and tested, Ray, and my faith is unshakable. Will you add your faith to mine? That would surely speed up the process."

"Oh, you bet!" Ray said, grinning. "I'll move that mountain over there, too, if you just ask. Right now. Immediately. Just say the word, and it's done."

Laura laughed then, Ray grinned even wider, and the remainder of the ride home was relaxed and enjoyable.

8

When Laura asked her the next day, Shelli could not remember what she had been trying to tell her mother the day of the fire. All she could remember seeing were flames where the little bed had been. She had no recollection of Krystal's location at that time.

Laura was certain that Shelli had seen more, but she decided not to push her, not to cause her to have worse memories of the event than she already had.

And that was an interesting thing, Laura reflected, as she started in on her ironing. None of the children seemed to have bad memories. There had been no nightmares, no apparent emotional traumas. The priesthood blessings given by her parents' home teachers had certainly been effective as far as the children were concerned. Why hadn't her blessing brought the same peace to her?

As Laura worked in her home that morning she thought of Ray, of what he had said the day before, and of his beautiful prayer that night. Interestingly, he had not prayed for himself, or even for both of them. He had prayed only for her, pleading that her mind would be comforted and that the righteous desires of her heart would be granted.

Laura was certain that her desire to see Krystal was a righteous one. She felt she had to know how much Krystal had suffered. Above all, she had to know whether her daughter had forgiven her. In fact, that question had become the most important issue in her life, and she desperately needed to have it resolved. The Lord would surely understand that, especially after Ray's prayer. Laura knew he would. And he would allow Krystal to appear, too. Oh, it would be so good to know and to finally be at peace!

And when she saw her daughter, there were so many things she wanted to ask. Had Krystal's death been planned long before? Was there someone there to meet her? Had she suffered in the fire? And finally, if Laura could have saved her and hadn't, would she still be accepted as her mother?

All that morning Laura's thoughts were upon Krystal and on the never-ending agony she herself had experienced in the days and weeks since her daughter's death. At noon when Ray came home for lunch he asked her how she was getting along, and Laura eagerly told him what she was feeling.

"I know she'll come, Ray. I feel very assured that I will see her. And I feel that it will be today."

"Well, I hope so, Laura. For your sake I hope so. But if she doesn't appear, don't be too disappointed. The Lord can answer your prayers in any way he chooses, you know. In fact, I think the Lord must run heaven the way I run my business."

"What? Ray, what on earth are you talking about?"

"Economy, Laura. I run my business economically, and I suspect that heaven is run in the same way. Visions are probably very expensive items there. I'd guess the Lord uses them sparingly. When he can, he communicates by other, less expensive means. You know, like impressions and inspirations and so on. All I'm saying, honey, is that I hope you're prepared to accept his word no matter how it comes."

"Of course I will, sweetheart. But where did you ever get such a funny idea?"

"The idea wasn't mine, Laura. It was Elder Neal Maxwell's."

"Oops! Boy, did I blow that! Sorry I laughed."

"Yeah, I'll bet you are!"

"I am. Honest. But Ray, I'm still sure that I'll see her."

"Well, I hope so. I really do. Anyway, guess I'd better get back to work. I'll see you later, honey."

"Bye-bye."

As Ray was leaving, he turned and asked Laura if she would have time to stop at the post office for him. When she nodded yes, Ray smiled, climbed into his truck, blew her a kiss, and drove off.

For a moment Laura thought of her husband's special, funny ideas, and she then smiled as she offered a small prayer of gratitude for him.

"Economy in heaven," she said aloud as she returned to her work and her waiting. "I wonder if Elder Maxwell really did say that?"

The hours passed, and with their passing Laura grew increasingly concerned. By late afternoon, when nothing had happened, she knew she could postpone her errands no longer.

Thoroughly disappointed, she packed Jenni into the car and drove to the supermarket. As she was pushing her cart down the aisle, feeling more depressed than she had felt since Krystal's death, someone behind her called her name. Turning, she saw one of her closest friends hurrying toward her.

"Laura," the woman said breathlessly, "do you have a minute? There's something I've got to tell you."

The woman then told Laura that after she had heard of the accident she couldn't get Krystal out of her mind. She was so worried that she went to her bedroom, knelt in prayer, and asked God concerning her fears. She asked if Krystal had suffered, if she was frightened, if she was alone, and if there was someone there to meet her when she died. The woman felt impressed that there had been other spirit beings in attendance at the fire and that all was right with Krystal.

When the woman had gone, Laura numbly completed her shopping and checked out at the cashier stand. "Other spirits," she thought over and over. "Other spirits were in attendance at my baby's death. She was not *alone!* She was not afraid! While I watched the bus burning, there were others there, beings from the spirit world who . . ."

"Laura, are you going to write a check or take a nap?"

Startled, Laura realized that the cashier, another friend, had finished and was waiting to be paid. Feeling a little embarrassed at her total preoccupation, she smiled, apologized, and wrote out the check.

As she left the store and drove to the post office, she found herself once again deep in thought, ignoring Jenni's constant "guess what" questions. Her mind was totally absorbed with thoughts of spirits and of Krystal. Somehow, she realized, she had never thought of Krystal as being associated with other spirit beings.

At the post office Laura noticed that she was nearly out of gas, so on her way home she stopped at the filling station. Then, as she was inside the station paying the bill, she was surprised to see a good family friend standing at the window of her car talking to Jenni.

"Hey, Laura," he said as she walked up. "How are you getting along?"

Laura smiled. "I'm doing fine," she replied.

"Do you know," her friend continued, "I've been meaning to come and see you folks so I could tell you what happened to me. But one thing led to another, and I just haven't taken the time. Anyway, when I saw Jenni I decided to wait for you. Do you have a minute?"

Laura nodded.

The man continued. "I was praying one night, shortly after Krystal died, and I felt strongly that she hadn't suffered in the fire. I didn't hear any voices or anything, you understand. I was just somehow told. Anyway, something happened that she didn't suffer. Of course, I expect you and Ray knew that, but I just wanted you to know of my experience."

Totally amazed at the apparent coincidence of two dear friends meeting her and sharing essentially the same information on the same afternoon, Laura drove somberly homeward. As she wound her way through town, she found herself wondering if Ray had somehow set it up. But he couldn't have, and she knew it. He hadn't even known her schedule.

When Laura pulled into the driveway, she could see that Ray was not yet home, so she asked the children if they would like to ride with her out to the cemetery. They all gave enthusiastic agreement to that suggestion, so once the groceries were put away and their coats snugly done up against the cold, they all piled into the car.

At the cemetery they stood together in silence, gazing at the spot where Krystal lay. A cold north wind blew against them and there was the feel of snow in the air.

"Mommy," Jenni asked, finally breaking the silence, "doesn't Krystal get cold and lonely down there in the ground?"

"No, silly," Shelli replied with great authority. "She's not really there. Only her body is down there. Krystal is up in heaven with Heavenly Father."

"You're not my mommy," Jenni said quickly.

"No, she isn't, Jenni," Laura replied, "but still she is right. Krystal *is* in heaven."

"Is it warm there?" Jenni then inquired.

"Of course it is," Kari said quietly. "It's always summer in heaven."

"Jenni," Laura asked, "why did you wonder if Krystal was cold?"

"Because when I got my coat I saw hers. I'm cold, and I was afraid she would be, too."

"Oh, that is so thoughtful, Jenni. But don't worry. Shelli and Kari are right. Krystal isn't cold anymore."

For a few moments more they stood in silence. And then, as they turned to leave, Shelli darted directly in front of her mother, almost tripping her. The incident reminded Laura again of the fire, and of when she had almost tripped over Kari Lyn. That had been when she was still trying to see back through the flames, still trying unsuccessfully to see Krystal.

"Shelli, are you certain you can't remember anything about what happened to Krystal?"

Shelli started to shake her head, but then a light came into her eyes and she began to speak excitedly.

"I remember seeing Krystal, Mommy. She was on the bed when Daddy jumped off to try and fix the gas bottle. When Daddy jumped, Krystal suddenly fell over, her eyes closed, and she looked like she was asleep. She didn't move anymore, even a little. Then the bottle exploded. When I looked back, there wasn't any bed. It was all on fire. Krystal wasn't there anymore, either. She was gone. Fire was all over and I couldn't see her anywhere! So I grabbed Jenni and ran out!"

Later, as Laura told Ray what her two friends had said and what Shelli had recalled, it was immediately apparent to both of them that the Lord had answered each of Laura's questions. He hadn't sent Krystal, which disappointed Laura; but he had nevertheless responded to her needs.

Obviously the propane bottle had been spraying directly beneath Krystal's bed, and from Shelli's description the baby apparently had breathed the propane fumes, which had rendered her instantly unconscious. She wouldn't even have known that there was a fire. And that was why she had not cried out. She was already gone when the bottle actually exploded. Krystal had not suffered!

9

As the days passed, Laura was surprised that the peace she had expected from her new-found knowledge did not come. True, some of the things that had bothered her no longer caused concern. But new things sprang up, new thoughts and worries that would not leave her alone. Those, coupled with her persistent, nagging feeling of guilt, made her wonder at times if she was losing her testimony. In spite of all the blessings which Heavenly Father had given her, she continued to feel responsible for her baby's death. And though she almost hated herself for feeling that way, she did not know how to change.

One new thing that bothered her, the biggest thing, was the thought of Krystal's charred and burned little body. Before burying her child, Laura recalled how she had yearned to see her. But family and friends had dissuaded her, telling her that she needed to remember Krystal as she had been before the fire.

Now, however, Laura felt that they had been wrong. She had needed to see her baby's body. She had needed to know exactly how badly it had been burned. Of course, she realized that

Krystal's body would have been badly damaged, and she cringed each time she thought of it. But still her mind kept going back . . . back . . . Only now it was too late, though, forever too late. Krystal was buried, and Laura would never know the answer to this question.

One night, while lying in bed, Laura asked Ray if he thought it would be all right if she were to ask the fireman who had found Krystal how badly she had been burned.

For a few moments her husband didn't answer, and Laura had almost decided he was asleep. But then finally he spoke.

"I don't think you should ask him, Laura."

"But why, Ray? He would know."

"Honey, can't you remember the expression on his face as he carried Krystal from the bus? That man went through his own personal hell that day, and I don't think it would be right, asking him to relive the experience. Do you?"

"Well, no. Not when you put it like that. But Ray, I've got to *know*! It's all I can think about. Somebody needs to tell me. Oh, if only Krystal would return. She could put my mind at ease so quickly. Why doesn't Heavenly Father let her come back?"

"I don't know, Laura. I really don't. I only know that you've got to stop worrying about it so much."

"I can't, Ray. Not until I know. And I'll know as soon as I see Krystal. Can't you understand that?"

"Oh, I understand it, honey. But I'm not sure it's right. It seems to me that you aren't exercising much faith."

"What do you mean? How can you say that, Ray?"

"Well Laura, your patriarchal blessing counsels you to bear great personal sacrifice without complaint. And you know what a marvelous promise the Lord made to you if you do. But now you've made a personal sacrifice, a very great one, and it seems to me that you're complaining about it. Doesn't that show a lack of faith?"

"Maybe . . . But Ray, I can't help it. I've got to see her. Won't that require faith?"

"Sure it will, Laura. Lots of it, only . . . is it the right kind of faith? I just don't know if you're asking for the right thing."

"Ray, what are you saying? Can't you see what's happening inside me? I'm being torn to pieces, and I can't do anything about it. No one can help me. No one but Krystal. Ray, I'm going to continue pleading for help until she comes. But it hurts me when I hear you say that I don't have much faith."

"Hey, honey," Ray said. "I didn't mean to hurt you. I know you have faith. In fact, you have so much faith that it worries me."

"Worries you? Why?"

"Because I like you here beside me. I'd be awfully frustrated if I reached over to kiss you and 'phoof!' you got translated on me. How do you kiss a wife who's going up through the ceiling?"

"Oh, Ray, you're terrible!"

"Well, really, Laura, I'm partly serious. Your faith scares me to death sometimes. I'd never dare ask for what you're asking for. But listen. If you're really serious, why don't we do what we did before? Let's tell the Lord about it and turn it over to him."

"Well, I have, lots of times. But —"

"But nothing. Come on, Laura. Let's do it together. If we add my thimble-full of faith to your bushel, we're bound to get results."

One week later, when Laura had almost given up hope of having her prayer answered, she attended a friend's wedding reception. As she was visiting with some other people, she saw the mortician who had cared for Krystal's body.

Immediately Laura realized that he could tell her what she so desperately needed to know. As she thought about it, though, she knew that she couldn't ask him, not on such a happy occasion. Yet, oh, how she longed to speak with him about her daughter!

Later, as she prepared to leave, the mortician saw her, approached, and asked if he could talk with her about Krystal's death.

Laura, stunned, simply stared as the man explained that he had wanted to speak to her for some time but hadn't because of the pain he knew she must be feeling.

"Oh, please," Laura responded, nearly in tears with hope. "Would you? I have to know. How badly was she burned? Could you tell that she was even a baby? Were her arms and legs there? Was she buried in a body bag, or did someone wrap her in a blanket?"

The thought of a body bag had especially bothered Laura. She had always felt that if she lost one of her children, she would want to dress her herself. She wanted to be the one to comb the child's hair and wrap her favorite blanket around her. Krystal deserved better than to be shoved into a body bag and left in the ground.

In response to Laura's questions, the mortician told her that he had washed and cleaned Krystal's little body. Then he had wrapped her in a little pink receiving blanket and laid her in the coffin.

"Oh, thank you so much," Laura said, tears coming to her eyes. "Thank you for caring about my baby."

As the man continued, telling her how badly Krystal had been burned, Laura realized that she had imagined it to be much worse than it was. The little body was charred, but it was all there, easily recognizable as a baby girl. Laura realized that such a thing would normally sound terrible, but the knowledge he gave her brought much peace to her soul.

"Laura," the mortician said gently. "There is more. Can you bear to listen a little longer?"

She quickly nodded, and so he continued.

"When I was called to the hospital, I had no idea that it was a baby who had died. I had just been asked to pick up a body. When I got there, the nurse was having a difficult time emotionally. She told me that it was a baby girl, and that she had been burned. I asked where she was from and the nurse told me. Then, when she told me who the parents were, I was shocked and saddened. They were people I knew.

"I took the body and placed it in my car to drive to Salt Lake

City to the coroner's office. Before I left, I stopped and talked with the ambulance drivers, who told me a little more about what had happened. They were really shaken by the death of this baby. When I reached my car, Laura, I cried.

"When I arrived in Salt Lake City, I found that the people in the coroner's office there were upset by your baby's death, which also seemed strange to me. I couldn't understand that. What was there about this child, I wondered, that even in death she could touch so many people?

"All the way home I kept thinking, What a horrible accident! Even after I took her body to the mortuary and began preparing it for burial, that was all I could think about.

"But then her spirit came, and she stood by me, watching me care for her body. I didn't see her, but I could very much feel her. She was not a baby but was instead a full-grown woman. Somehow she made it known to me that her death was not an accident. It had been the will of Heavenly Father. Krystal was serene, and she was very much at peace with what had happened. After that, I didn't feel so badly."

Weeping, Laura thanked the man for his sensitivity in sharing his experience with her. She was deeply grateful that her prayers had been answered.

And yet even with all the answers she had received, Laura still felt an overwhelming need to see and visit with her daughter.

THREE

10

"Laura, you can't!"

It was late, the children were all in bed, and Ray was becoming more frustrated by the moment.

"You know how sick you get when you fast. It isn't right for you to do it, especially for three or four days."

"Ray," Laura pleaded, "please try to understand. I *have* to do this. I must see my baby, and I don't know of any other way to show the Lord that I'm sincere."

"But, honey, you have to be a wife and a mother too. It's pretty hard to fill those roles properly when you're sick. Besides, there's another problem you might not have thought of, a problem that could be much more serious. *I* know you love our other children as much as you love Krystal, but *they* might not know that. All they ever see is a mother who seems to be obsessed with Krystal. She is almost all you ever think or talk about. How does that make them feel? I don't know, of course, but I do know how it makes me feel, and I'm beginning to resent it. Now you go on a three-day fast to see Krystal, and it makes you so sick that you don't want to see any of the rest of us for three days. Tell me, what kind of sense does that make?"

"None, I suppose. But I'm telling you this, Ray. If I don't get some peace soon, I never will be a decent wife *or* mother. I've got to see her, and this is the only way I can think of to do it."

"But you don't have to fast, Laura. Not when it makes you so sick. Just go to the temple. The Lord knows of your sincerity."

"Sweetheart, I love you for your concern, but I *must* fast. There must be no doubt in my mind that I have sacrificed totally. Only then can I exercise full faith, and only when I do that will Heavenly Father grant me my request. I promise you, dear, that you and the children won't suffer. You won't even know I'm fasting."

"Laura . . ."

"I love you, Ray. Good night."

Three days later, in the crispness of the early morning, Laura walked through the doors of the temple. She was weak, she was ill, and she was alone. Yet she was humbly and prayerfully determined to see her baby within the temple that day.

If the visit was going to take place, she reasoned, it would most likely be when she was through with the temple work. It would also most probably occur someplace where there was privacy. Yet Laura knew that asking permission to spend time alone in a temple room was discouraged. There were simply too many people who wanted that privilege, and not enough rooms to accommodate them.

But then Laura devised an interesting plan or test which would, she hoped, tell her what she wanted to know.

"Dear Father in Heaven," she prayed, "if I am to see Krystal today, please inspire one of the workers here to offer me a room so that I can be alone. Then I will know that you have granted me the right to see my daughter."

A little later, almost immediately after she had completed her assignment, Laura was approached by a woman who worked in the temple.

"Excuse me," the woman asked, "but would you like to be alone for a short time? This room over here will be vacant for the next thirty minutes."

Laura could hardly believe her ears. It had happened! Her little test had worked! She was to see her darling Krystal!

With her heart nearly in her throat Laura entered the room, closed the door, and knelt down. With all her might, then, she poured out her soul to her Heavenly Father, thanking him for his love, reminding him of her great burden, and waiting for her daughter to appear.

At first Laura was so excited and nervous that she could not hold back her tears. How would Krystal look, she wondered? Would she smile? Would she be able to talk? Would she have permission to answer questions? Would she be alone? Would she be able to show her love and affection?

Laura's nervous anticipation manifested itself in tears. However, as the seconds stretched into minutes, and as those grew longer and longer with no spiritual impressions or manifestations, the tears became tears of sorrow and confusion. "Why?" she cried out. "Why haven't I seen my baby?"

A short time later a soft knock on the door gave notice to Laura that her thirty minutes were over. Feeling thoroughly forsaken and alone, she left the temple, made her way to her car, and began the nearly three-hour drive home. For most of that distance Laura wept bitterly, unable to understand why she had been misled, why her request had been denied.

"Why?" she sobbed aloud. "Why did that woman come to me and ask me to go into that room? Wasn't that the test we'd agreed upon? Why am I being made to suffer so? Can't you see the faith I have? If the brother of Jared could not be kept outside of the veil, why do you keep me out? I know you could have allowed her to appear to me. I needed to see her."

As the miles slipped behind her, Laura found her thoughts going in circles, from thoughts of her childhood with her parents to her patriarchal blessing, to Krystal's birth, to the fire, to the funeral, and finally to her incomprehensible experience in the temple that day. Then they would start over, back to her parents again and her patriarchal blessing. What did it all mean? Why had everything happened as it had, and why had she been denied the right to see her daughter?

Ray said that someday they would see the blessing in all of it, but how could the personal agony she had lived through ever be construed as a blessing? Didn't God know what she was going through? Couldn't he understand her pain? If he truly loved her, as she had always believed, why would he want her to suffer such utter loneliness? It just didn't make sense.

Finally, when she was within a few miles of her home, Laura pulled off the road. She could go no further until she came to grips with her thoughts and emotions. Her tears at last were spent, as was her bitterness, and her spirit was more subdued than it had ever been. For some time she just sat, thinking of nothing in particular, simply feeling, praying, trying to comprehend.

At first she understood nothing, felt nothing. But then, after a time, she realized that a scripture from the Book of Mormon, one she had memorized years before in seminary, was being repeated over and over again in her mind.

"I would show unto the world," the prophet Moroni seemed to be declaring to her, "that faith is things which are hoped for and *not* seen; wherefore, dispute not because ye see not, for ye receive no witness until after the trial of your faith."

"But, but . . . ," Laura stammered, perhaps to herself, "what about what I have gone through? What about my daughter's death? If that wasn't a trial of my faith, then I don't know what was!"

For a moment more she was silent, thinking, waiting, hoping, praying. And then, into her mind, like pure sweet water, flowed a gentle, silent voice. Her ears didn't hear but her heart did, and Laura wept uncontrollably as she learned.

"Yes, my daughter," the voice said gently, "your faith has been tried. But you do not decide when the trial is over. *I* do. I paid the price. Now cease your murmuring and your doubting. I love you, and I have promised that all things will work together for your good if you walk uprightly. Trust in me, and they will."

And then the voice was gone and Laura was alone, alone with her thoughts of her parents, her tears, and her increased love for the Savior. She would see her daughter. She suddenly knew that. But she would not be the one to choose when. He would. And when it happened, it would be right.

Finally, when her weeping was mostly done, Laura took her journal from her purse and began to write.

"Oh, my little Krystal, how I miss you! How I long to see you! I just start thinking that I'm all right and then the loneliness floods back over me, engulfing me in sorrow. There was so much that I wanted to teach you, to share with you. I know you don't need that now, because you are much advanced in comparison to me. But my need to hold and cuddle you, to teach you, to rejoice in your presence, is still a part of me, very strong.

"Go forward, my little angel child. Climb to your eternal glory with our Heavenly Father. I love you! I'm so proud to have been honored to be your mother, to have made your beautiful little body. I'll follow behind as quickly as I am able to learn and to progress.

"How I love Jesus, my little Krystal! He is my Savior, my Redeemer, my Lord. He gave his life that I might have the privilege of spending eternity with you. Be patient while I learn to know him and to trust him as well as you do.

"Be patient too while I honor my commitment as mother to your brother and sisters. Their needs now are great, while yours are being met by heavenly parents whose capabilities are far superior to my own. Your earthly father also needs me, as I need him. Krystal, I now know that from today forward

I must focus my love and attention upon them. To do otherwise would be to deny Heavenly Father's love for us both, a love which he expressed through his Son's atonement.

"But dear Krystal, know that I love you with all my heart and soul. I do, and I will *never* forget you. I promise! You will always be my sweet, celestial baby.

"Forever and ever,
Your Mother"

Smiling then through her tears, Laura momentarily lifted her eyes heavenward.

"Thank you," she said softly. "I love you."

Then she started the car and pulled back onto the road, suddenly anxious to get home — home to Ray, and home to her beautiful, special children.

EPILOGUE

Today is Wednesday, it is 7:30 P.M., and we have just written the concluding words of the manuscript which we will title *The Krystal Promise*. As we look at each other across the desk, we realize that there is little need to speak. We are both feeling the same. Our hearts and our spirits are subdued, for never have either of us experienced anything quite like what we have just passed through.

Weeks ago, in response to a rather unusual, intensely spiritual invitation, we packed our pens and notepads and undertook a fascinating journey. Our destination was a very private, very peaceful place. It was located in the hearts and minds and spirits of a special yet excitingly normal family.

You see, the story you have just read, the story of Krystal, is based on truth. Krystal was/is/will be the youngest daughter of Bill and Lyla Brock, of Green River, Utah. Krystal is also the youngest sister of Tynna, Tory, Tandi, Misti and Cheri, the Brock children. While each of these family members stood helplessly by, tiny Krystal perished in an accidental fire.

It has been less than a year since this tragedy occurred, and it is still a painful memory. Even so, the family has felt impressed to share. Following her visit to the temple, Lyla felt strongly that she needed to write of her experience with the death of her baby. This was a painful process, yet through her faith she was able to complete it. And to her surprise Lyla found that when she had finished writing, her sorrow had been lifted, her experiences had focused clearly in her mind, and her soul was at peace. She then shared her written feelings and testimony with us.

How does one describe pain that one has not felt? How does one describe horror? or loneliness? or grief? or guilt? On the other hand, how does one describe faith? or hope? or love? Can spiritual yearnings, or spiritual impressions, be written by those who have not experienced them? Could an uplifting message come from such a devastating ordeal?

We sincerely wondered and anxiously worried. Yet there was a feeling, an urgent impression, to write. And so we did, moving into the private souls of these people as we began to live with them, moment by moment, the greatest trial of their lives thus far.

As we lived their trial we began to feel, and it wasn't long before we had the strange and frightening sensation of being one with them. And how do we write of that sort of experience? It cannot be done. It defies description, real though it was. We enjoyed, we felt, we wept, we ached, we yearned, we pleaded, we grew frustrated, and last of all, we learned. Oh, how we learned!

We have spent many hours in conversation with Lyla and Bill, and we have been touched by the sweetness of their spirits. Lyla loves her family more than her life, and she reverences and trusts her Heavenly Father totally. Bill, a fine man who uses words sparingly, feels the same. These two not only support, but sensitively lift each other.

"Lyla," we asked in a recent conversation, "what about now? Has the pain of loneliness begun to diminish?"

"No," she replied quietly. "It has changed somewhat, but it has not lessened. Nor do we suppose it ever will. We think that even God must yet feel pain when he thinks of the way his son suffered.

But as that suffering blessed the world, so our baby's death was an eternal blessing to her, as it is proving to be for us. She is celestial. We cannot feel badly about that."

"Would you change things if you could?" we asked.

"Well . . . no," Lyla responded, after a brief pause. "We really wouldn't. If God came to us today and asked us if we would like Krystal back, we would say 'Yes, but no.' As much as we would like her with us, we could not bear to take away her eternal happiness, nor would we dare thwart Heavenly Father's plan.

"Of course there are many times when we long to hold our baby. We will not deny that. We miss her with all of our hearts. But when the longing becomes too great to bear, the Lord sends his Spirit, the Comforter, to ease our loneliness. Occasionally he even allows us to feel Krystal's presence, as we have frequently during the writing of this book. Because of that, we are assured that Krystal wants our story written and shared with others. Perhaps it will prove to be a comfort to others who may be called to endure their own trials of faith, whatever they may be."

And perhaps it will. As the writers, we sincerely hope so.

Blaine and Brenton Yorgason